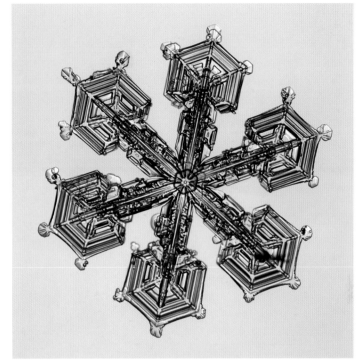

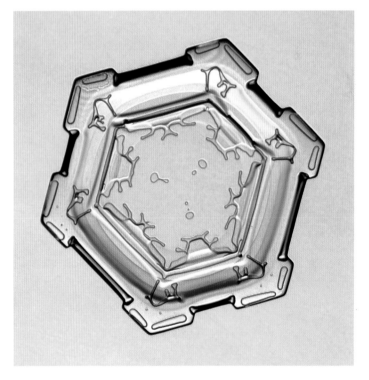

THE *Art* OF THE SNOWFLAKE

A Photographic Album

Kenneth Libbrecht

SWEET WATER PRESS

402 Industrial Lane
Birmingham, Alabama 35211

© 2013 Voyageur Press
Text and photography © 2007, 2013 Kenneth Libbrecht

This 2013 edition published by Sweet Water Press by arrangement with Voyageur Press, an imprint of MBI Publishing Company, 400 First Avenue North, Suite 400, Minneapolis, MN 55401 USA.

Editor: Michael Dregni
Designer: Jennifer Bergstrom

ISBN-13: 978-1-4682-6584-2

Printed in China

2 4 6 8 10 9 7 5 3 1

On the front cover: The four cover snowflakes were all photographed one cold January day in northern Ontario, when the clouds delivered a multitude of large, well-formed stellar crystals.

Under the microscope, I found that snowflakes were miracles of beauty; and it seemed a shame that this beauty should not be seen and appreciated by others. Every crystal was a masterpiece of design, and no one design was ever repeated. When a snowflake melted, that design was forever lost. Just that much beauty was gone, without leaving any record behind.

—Wilson Bentley (1865–1931)

Winter's Secret Beauty

Snowflakes are remarkable examples of nature's art. They are born within the grey winter clouds, where the simple act of freezing turns formless water vapor into spectacular crystalline ice sculptures. How amazing it is that these elaborate, symmetrical, and sometimes stunningly beautiful structures appear quite literally out of thin air!

For many years I have been studying the physics of how crystals form and patterns emerge during their growth. Snowflakes are one focus of this research, as their formation is a particularly fascinating case study of how complex structures can arise spontaneously, even from very simple precursors. Understanding the molecular processes that shape snowflakes is scientifically interesting in its own right, and it helps address more general questions about how complexity arises in nature.

Much of my work is done in the lab, creating tiny ice crystals under controlled conditions and measuring their growth. I use precision microscopy in these experiments, and over time I have developed some new techniques for capturing images of snow crystals that show their structure with unprecedented detail. I soon realized that this type of microscopy could provide better views of natural snow crystals as well.

As my interest in photographing snowflakes increased, I faced the problem that my home in Southern California is not exactly known for its snowy winters. So I built a special-purpose microscope that fits in a suitcase, and I began making photographic expeditions to the frozen north. This unusual hobby soon had me hooked. To date, I've taken more than 7,000 pictures of all types of snow crystals.

Equipped with my portable photo-microscope, I've journeyed to central Alaska, Vermont, the mountains of California, the Michigan Upper Peninsula, and throughout northern Ontario, all in search of photogenic snowflakes. Each location has its own unique climate and thus its own variety of crystals to offer.

Photographing snowflakes is always enjoyable because there are so many different types, with no two exactly alike. Each new snowfall is another world to explore, and I still often find novel specimens. The snow may seem rather unvaried to the naked eye, but the microscope reveals an amazing menagerie of beautiful crystalline forms.

The methods I use for finding and handling snowflakes are simple. If the falling crystals are large, I let them land on a dark foam-core collection board held at a convenient height using a tripod. I hunt around on this surface to find nice specimens, occasionally brushing it clear as I search. Even on a good day, most snowflakes are rather poorly formed, looking essentially like bits of icy gravel, so it can take some effort to find outstanding crystals. The biggest limiting factor in snowflake photography is simply what the skies have to offer.

When I find an especially photogenic snowflake, I pick it up using a small paintbrush and move it onto a glass slide. I often twirl the brush to roll its bristles gently under the crystal in order to lift it off the collection board. Once I've transferred it to the slide, I use the brush to lightly press the crystal as flat as possible against the glass surface so it will all be in focus in the picture. Handling snowflakes like this causes surprisingly little damage, although it does not yield perfect results every time. Fortunately, if a specimen breaks, there are plenty more to choose from.

Once a crystal is under the microscope, I have anywhere from a few minutes (on colder days) to a few seconds (on warmer days) to adjust the lighting, focus, and take the shot. Taking good pictures means taking a lot of pictures, and a good snowfall might yield a hundred or more in an afternoon. Everything must be done outside in the cold, and only my camera has the luxury of a heated enclosure to keep warm.

Often the crystals are not large enough to pick up, so then I switch methods and simply let them fall onto clean glass slides. Once a slide has a good dusting of snow, I place it under the microscope and scan around for interesting subjects. This straightforward technique has yielded many excellent pictures of smaller crystals, some with bizarre shapes, even in snowfalls when I first thought there was little worth photographing.

I try to record whatever each snowfall has to offer, looking for good examples of all different snowflake types. Beautifully formed stellar crystals are always a delight to find and photograph, but the clouds deliver many other remarkable forms as well. I always keep a lookout for exotic and curious specimens. My goal throughout these outdoor adventures is to capture as much as I can of all the fascinating variety and beauty of snow crystal structures and patterns.

Observing and photographing snowflakes is an unusual pursuit, but I enjoy it immensely. Seeing these spectacular crystalline ice sculptures under the microscope, each one unique, as they float slowly down all around is its own special thrill. Nature provides so much to see and ponder, even in the cold winds of winter.

And here comes the snow,
A language in which no word is ever repeated.
—William Matthews (1942–1997)

Snowflakes are made of ice, which is clear and colorless. When photographing, I typically shine colored lights through the crystals from behind to reveal their internal structure and accentuate detail. The ice acts like a complex lens that refracts the light, highlighting the various ridges, ribs, bubbles, and dimples that are present in most snowflakes.

The two photographs on this page show the same crystal under different lighting. For the picture on the left I used rather plain light, shining in mainly from one side, to produce a simple shadowing effect. For the picture above I used a rainbow of bright colors incident from different angles to yield a dark background with flamboyant highlights. Using light and color to accentuate detail is an important part of the art of snowflake photography.

These two pairs of pictures again show how an individual snow crystal can change its appearance when viewed under different types of lighting.

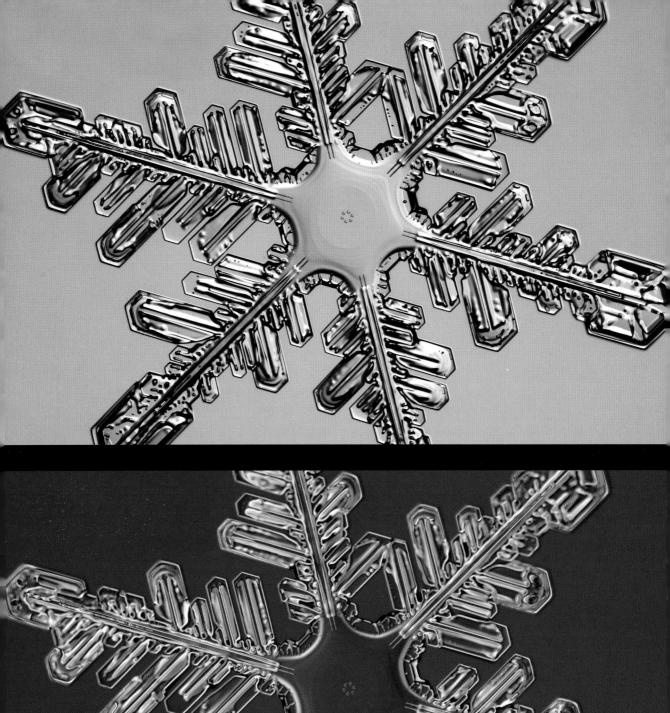
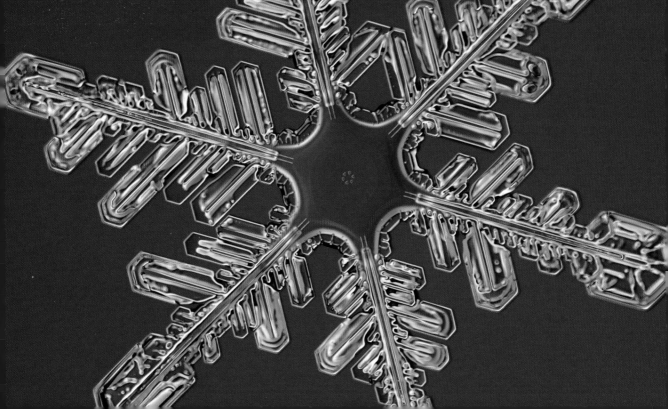

The Wonder of Snowflakes

Perhaps the most striking property of these diminutive ice flowers is that their structures are amazingly complex while also exhibiting a distinctive six-branched symmetry. What are the origins of these elaborate designs, and why do snowflakes form in such varied, symmetrical shapes? How is it that the clouds command such artistry?

The story of a snow crystal begins with the water that evaporates from lakes, forests, and oceans. Water vapor joins the air and is carried over great distances by the wind. If a parcel of warm, moist air happens to cool down, the water vapor it contains can condense onto ever-present dust particles in the air, forming tiny water droplets. The effect is essentially the same as when water condenses as dew drops on the grass when the evening air cools. The drifting clouds are nothing more than countless water droplets suspended in the air, each having formed around a minute speck of dust.

If a cloud cools enough, some of its constituent droplets will freeze. At the atomic level, freezing causes the water molecules to abandon their disordered liquid structure and connect together to form a solid latticework. Each molecule is obliged to attach just one way to its neighbors, resulting in a structure where all the molecules are precisely oriented with respect to one another. In the case of ice, this produces a hexagonal lattice because of the specific geometry of the water molecule; this molecular construction is what underlies the symmetry seen in snow crystals.

When a cloud droplet first freezes, it retains its roughly spherical shape, with little symmetry in its outward appearance. As more water vapor condenses onto the ice surface, however, the crystal grows and its hexagonal destiny begins to emerge.

The condensing molecules do not attach at all locations with equal likelihood. Chemical forces attract molecules to spots with the most dangling bonds. The molecular rows and columns tend to fill in before new rows and columns are added. With time, this yields faceted surfaces on the crystal, and the orientation of the different facets reflects the underlying lattice structure. This process is how the geometry of the water molecule ultimately guides the symmetry of a large snow crystal. Faceting tends to dominate the growth dynamics when crystals are small, so the tiniest snowflakes are likely to have a simple hexagonal shape.

As a snow crystal grows larger, simple faceted growth becomes impossible. The corners of a hexagonal crystal stick out farther into the humid air, so they tend to accumulate more water molecules and grow out a bit faster. The extra growth causes the corners to stick out even farther, which again increases their growth. There is a positive feedback effect, and soon six branches sprout from an initially hexagonal crystal. As these grow larger, the same process can yield side-branches on each of the main branches.

Once branches and side-branches appear, their subsequent growth is very sensitive to the temperature and humidity surrounding the crystal. Even a slight change in its local environment causes a change in the way the crystal grows. As it blows to and fro inside a cloud, a developing snowflake sees ever-changing conditions, so its final structure can be quite complex. And since each crystal follows its own unique path as it grows and descends, each arrives at the ground with a unique shape.

But while different snow crystals follow different paths through the clouds, the six branches of a single crystal travel together. They all experience the same growth history, so they grow in synchrony. The end result is a snow crystal that is both complex and symmetrical . . . and often quite stunning.

By considering the path of a single snow crystal, we see that its structure is not designed or predetermined in any way, but results from the random path it followed through the clouds as it grew. The arms are not synchronized by any mysterious force, but grow independently under nearly identical conditions.

The unruly whorls and eddies in the air drive each snowflake through a chaotic, convoluted path as it grows, resulting in a great diversity of final patterns. In this way, the wind becomes the artist, creating a multitude of unique ice sculptures using only the simplest of raw materials.

Given this picture of how snow crystals develop, one can estimate how many different structural variations are possible for a large, branched snowflake. The number is almost unfathomably large—so large, in fact, that I can say with confidence that no two complex snow crystals have ever been, or ever will be, exactly alike.

December 30, 2003: Timmins, Ontario
We rode the train from Moose Factory to Cochrane this morning, crossing a vast and sparsely populated expanse of boreal forest. Cochrane welcomed us with some flurries, so I hurriedly set up my camera outside the train station to work the snowfall. After a late lunch, we continued traveling south by car to Timmins. The snow returned in the evening, and again I found some excellent subjects to photograph. Working at night has its advantages, as the most attractive crystals advertise their presence by the sparkle of their facets reflecting the overhead street lamps.

It is surely one of nature's more inconspicuous extravagances that such enormous tracts of frozen landscape are so casually littered with these ephemeral works of art. I captured and recorded just a handful with my camera, while countless numbers fell unnoticed among the trees.

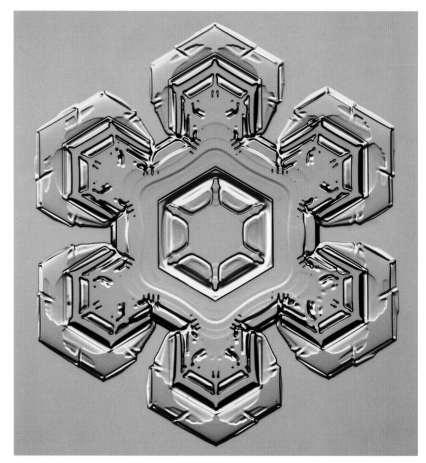

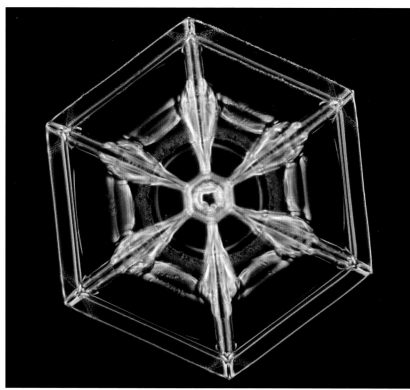

$\mathscr{S}$imple $\mathscr{P}$lates and $\mathscr{P}$risms

Small snow crystals are often faceted, looking like thin hexagonal plates or blocky hexagonal prisms. Although smaller than the head of a pin, each of these tiny crystals is decorated with unique surface patterns.

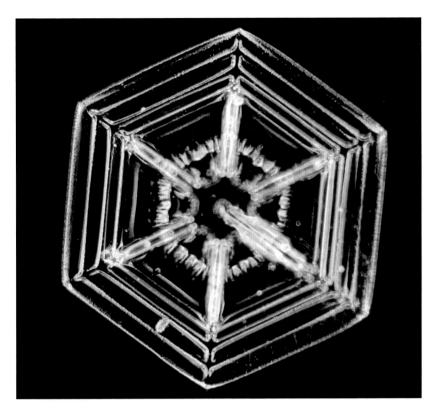
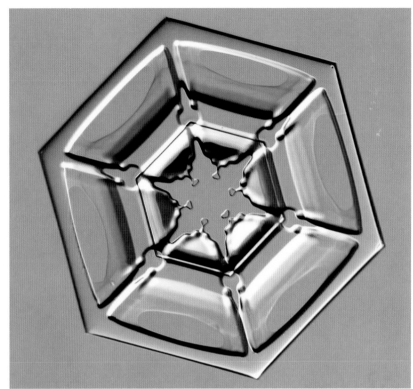
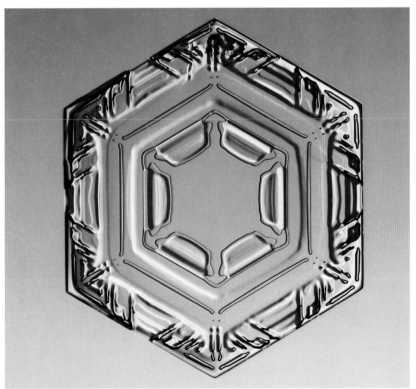

In all things of nature there is something of the marvelous.
—Aristotle (384 BC–322 BC)

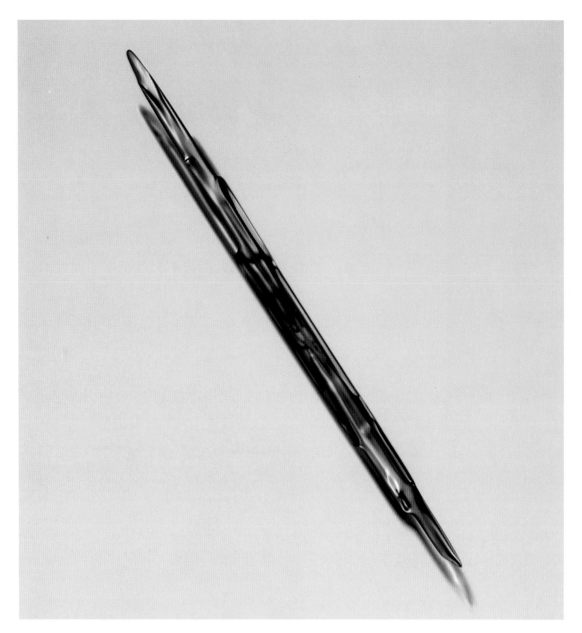

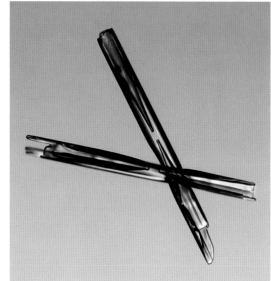

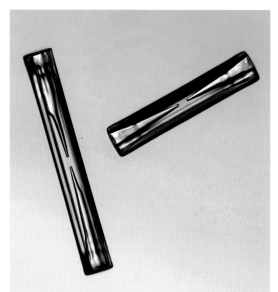

Columns and Needles

Warmer snowfalls often bring crystals shaped like slender hexagonal columns—the same basic form as wooden pencils. Often the columns have hollow ends, and some are long and thin, like tiny ice needles. These types of crystals are common, looking like short bits of white hair on your sleeve.

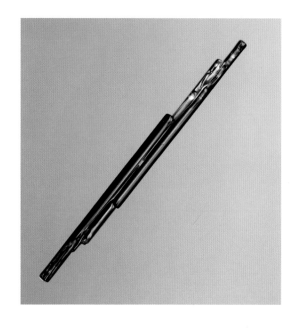

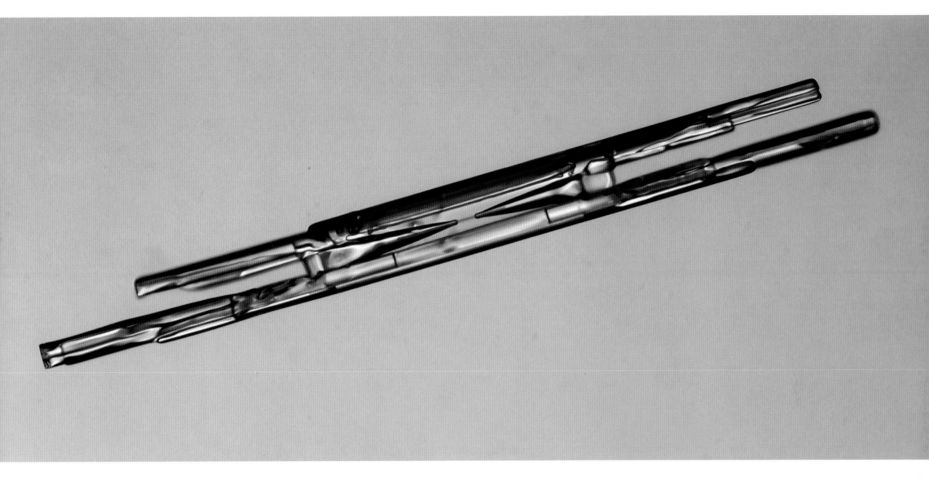

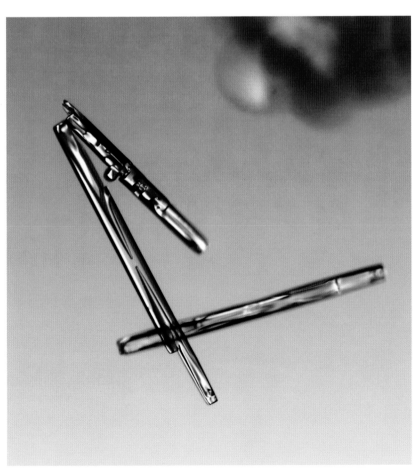

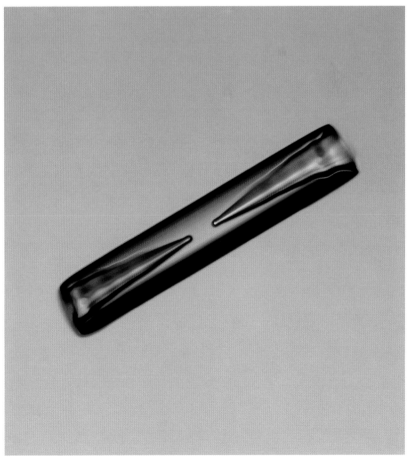

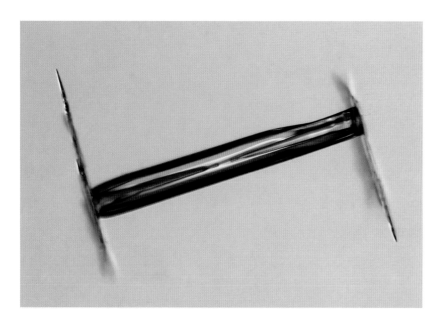

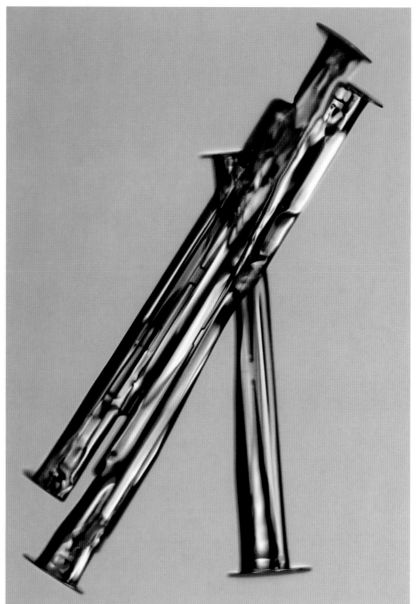

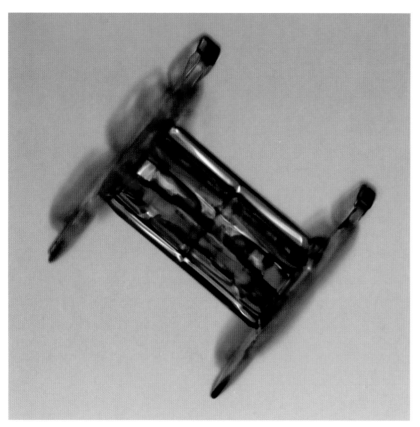

Capped Columns

These exotic snow crystal forms occur when the growth changes from columnar to plate-like in mid-flight. The archetypical example looks like a stubby axle flanked by two hexagonal wheels. They are relatively uncommon, but you can find them if you look for them.

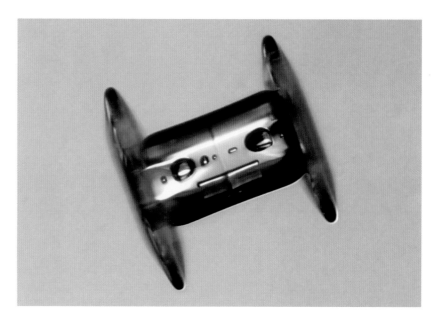

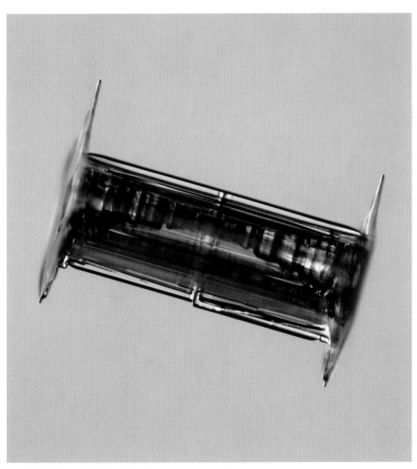

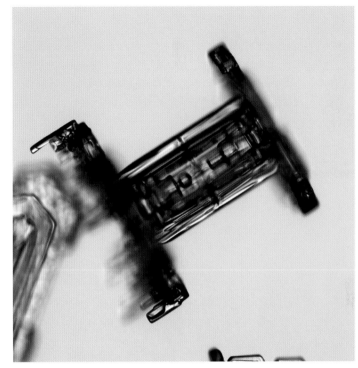

January 23, 2004: Fairbanks, Alaska

Visiting Fairbanks in January feels a bit like visiting another planet—one that's far from the sun. Even at noon, the sun seems distant as it peaks just a few degrees above the horizon. The 40-below-zero temperatures (sometimes colder!) make the snow squeak and crunch underfoot like some kind of brittle styrofoam. Car exhaust freezes instantly when it encounters the frigid air, filling the city with an ice fog that makes it difficult, at times, to see across the street. On clear nights, one can witness spectacular auroras, with brief periods where intense reds and greens fill the starry sky and dance wildly overhead.

The bitter cold snap ended yesterday, and this morning the weather brought a bounty of beautiful snow crystals. The snowfall started while it was still dark, so I picked out good specimens by porch light. The crystals were small, but many were well formed with strong angular features and excellent symmetry. The temperature hovered around -18 degrees Celsius (0 degrees Fahrenheit)—warmer than it's been, but still mercilessly cold on my bare fingers after several hours of collecting. As dawn broke slowly, I found there were no clouds to feed the snowfall, which explained why the crystals were small. For about an hour, the cold air was filled with countless effervescent sparkles reflecting the low sunlight as I hurriedly captured what I could.

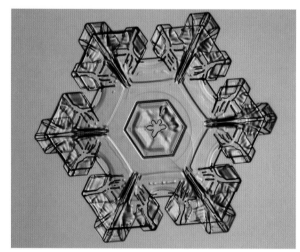

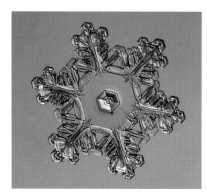

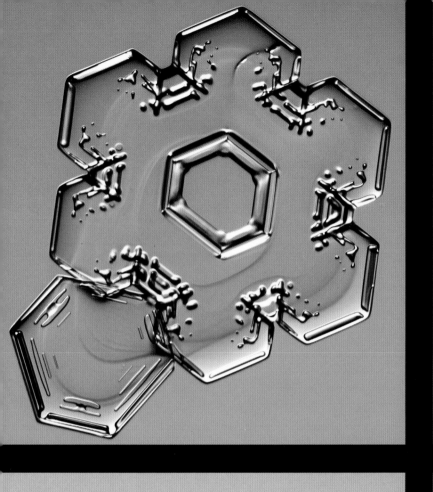

Sectored Plates

Hexagonal plates and broad-branched stellar plates are often decorated with ridges that appear to divide each crystal or its branches into sectors. These snow crystal forms are called sectored plates. Good specimens can be hard to find, although ridges are a common feature on many snowflakes.

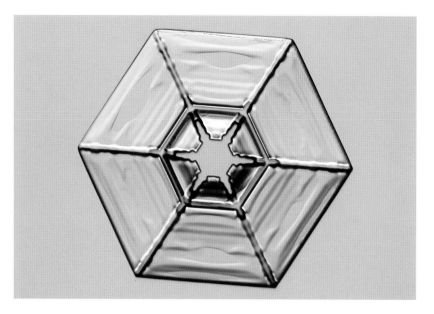

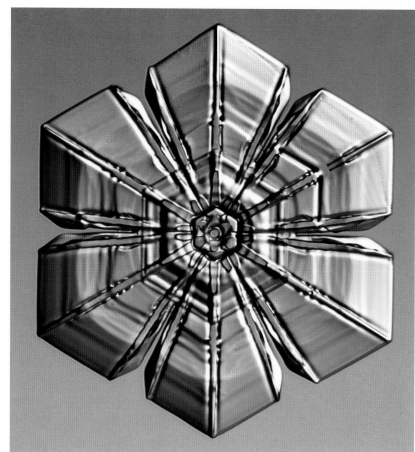

Stellar Plates and Stellar Dendrites

The canonical winter icons, stellar snow crystals are thin plates of ice with six main arms, or branches. When each main branch contains several sidebranches, the crystals are called stellar dendrites, which means "tree-like." In extreme cases, the crystals look like tiny ice ferns and are called fernlike stellar dendrites.

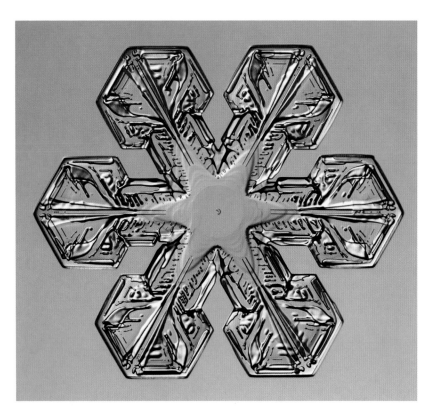

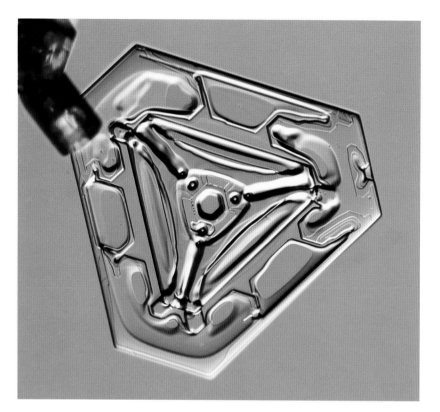
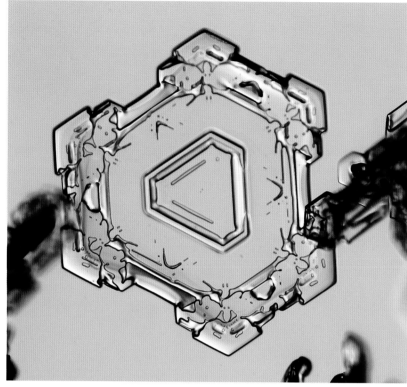
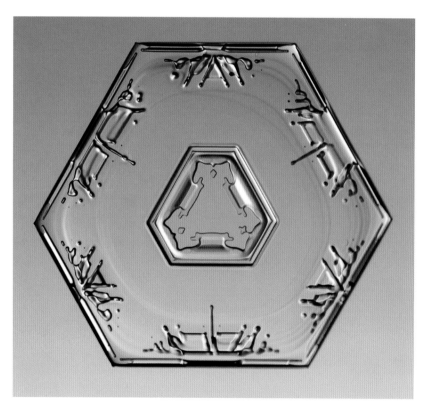
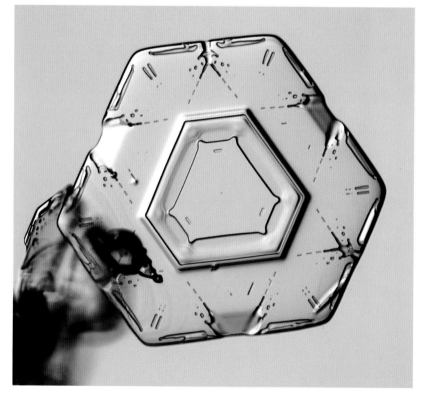

Triangular Crystals

On rare occasions, you can find some snow crystals showing a three-fold symmetry. These small crystals generally start out looking like truncated triangles.

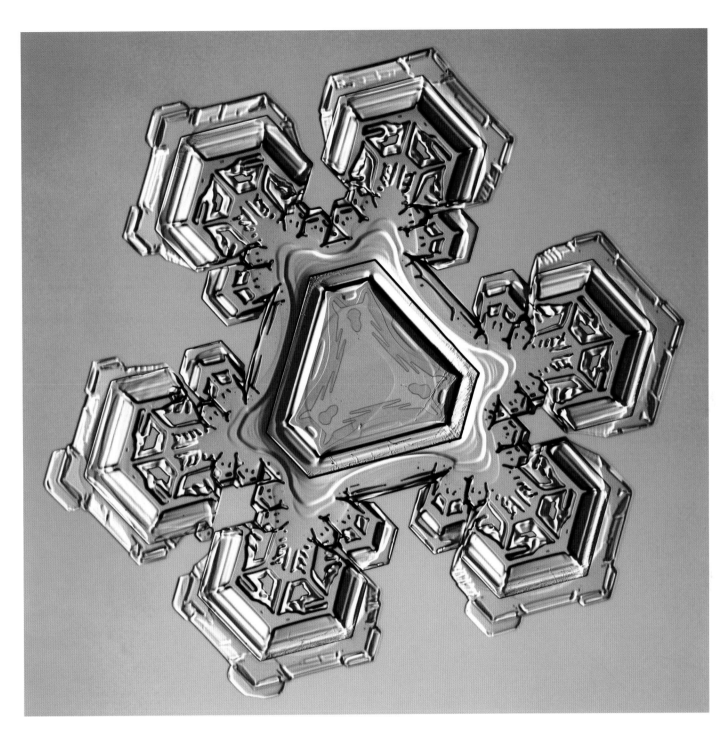

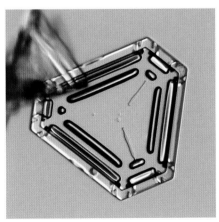
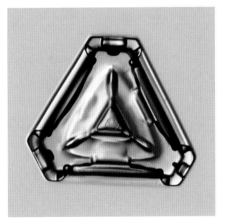

Twelve-branched Snowflakes

These rare, multilayered snow crystals consist of two six-branched stars joined at the center with a 30-degree twist. The two layers give the appearance of a 12-branched stellar snow crystal. The example at the top of this page (two photos of the same crystal) contains yet a third layer in the form of a small stellar plate.

Nature is ever at work building and pulling down, creating and destroying, keeping everything whirling and flowing, allowing no rest but in rhythmical motion, chasing everything in endless song out of one beautiful form into another.

—John Muir (1838–1914)

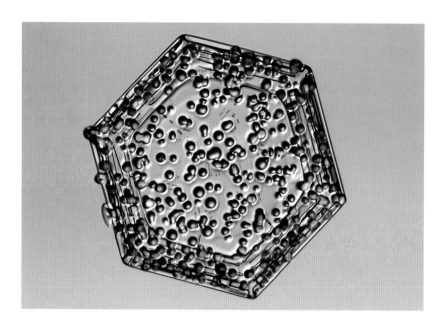

Rime and Graupel

Snowflakes are born in the clouds, and cloud droplets often bombard the crystals like miniature buckshot, freezing and sticking to the ice surfaces on contact. The frozen droplets are called rime, and many snowfalls contain little other than heavily rimed crystals. Precipitation that is made mostly of agglomerated rime particles is called graupel, or soft hail. The overall shapes of the crystals on this page reveal that they were all fully formed, symmetrical snow crystals before becoming coated with rime.

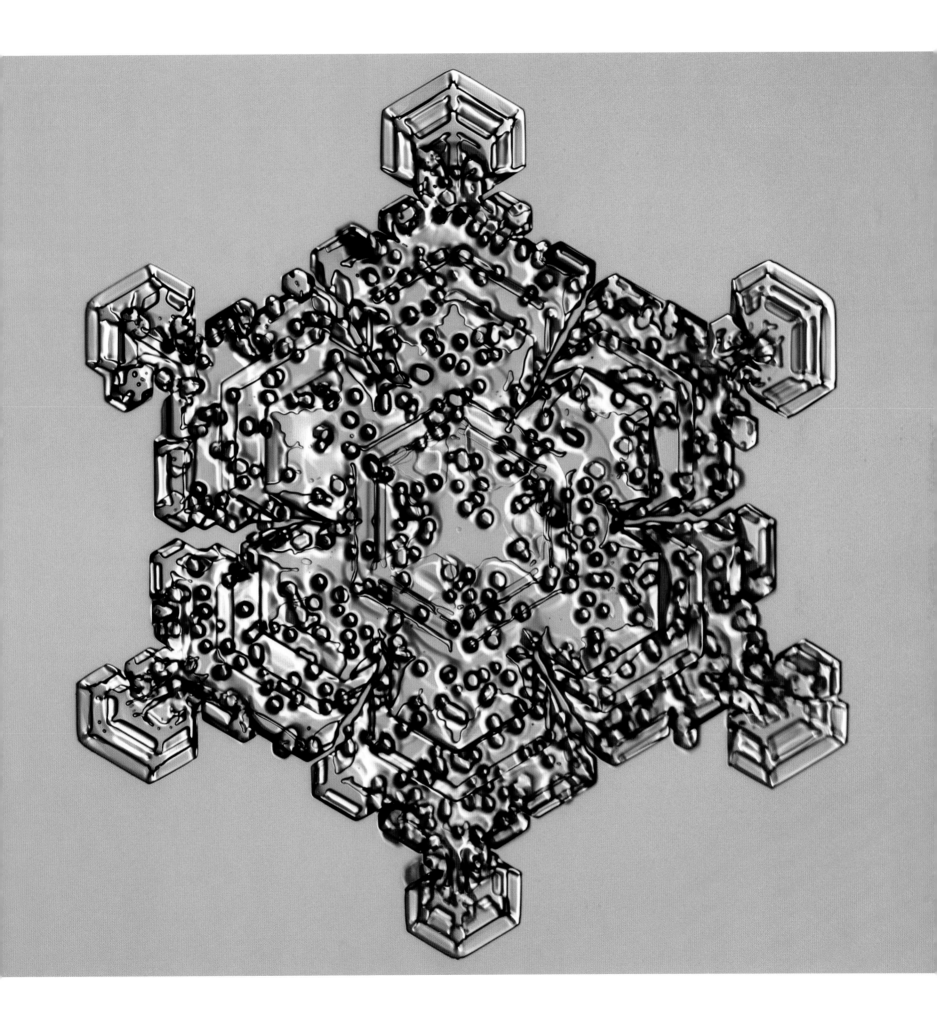

December 19, 2004: Burlington, Vermont

It was a blustery New England day today—cold with gusty winds. Lake Champlain, still retaining some of its autumn warmth, was giving off a dense fog. By early evening the wind had died down and a light snow began. I set up on the rooftop of my hotel parking structure, which had some bright lights to work under. It was a convenient location, although I did get odd looks from some pleasantly inebriated passersby.

At first the crystals arrived with thick rime coatings, but the rime diminished as the evening progressed. Just before midnight, the crystals became quite nice and I got some excellent pictures.

I couldn't help but think of Wilson Bentley, taking the very first snowflake photographs in the late 1800s from his farm just down the road near Jericho. We both captured the recycled fogs of Lake Champlain, brought back to earth as frozen ice crystals. The cycle continues with the seasons, yet each resulting snowflake is unique.

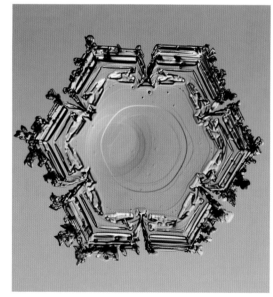

Double Plates

The crystals on this page are all made from pairs of thin, plate-like stellar crystals that are connected at their centers by short columns. They are basically capped columns where the end plates are close together and different sizes. When you look closely, a surprising number of plate-like snow crystals are actually made of two or more layers.

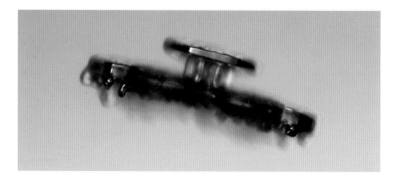

Split Plates and Split Stars

These odd-looking crystals began as double plates, but then part of one plate grew larger along with the complementary part of the other plate. The end result is two partial plates or stars connected by a small axle in the center. Split plates and stars, like double plates, are actually quite common.

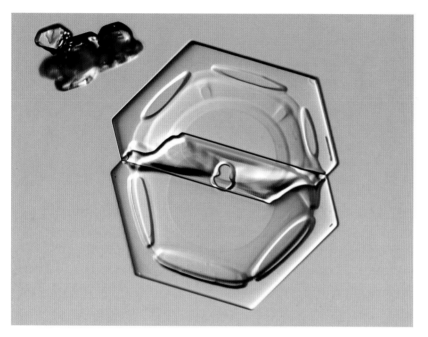

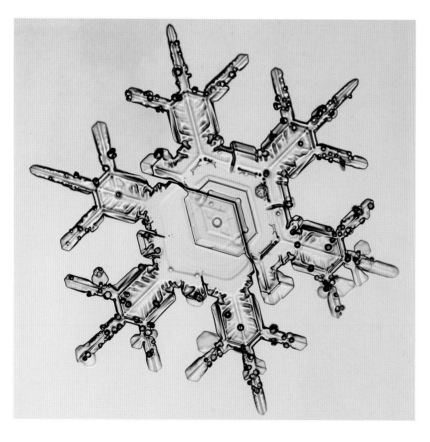

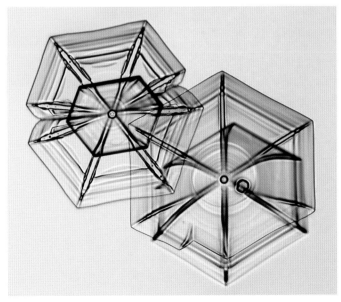

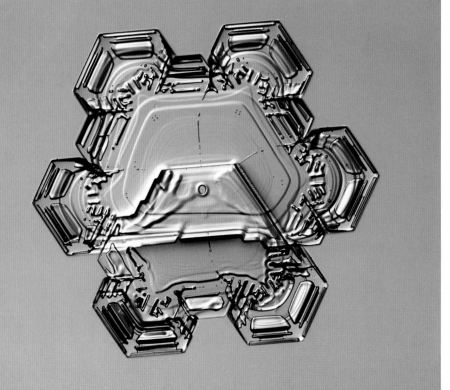

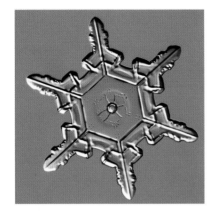 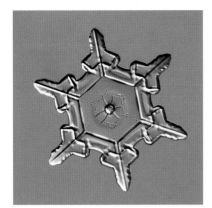 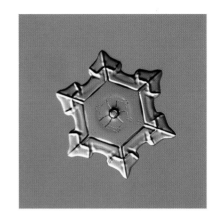 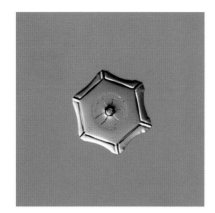

   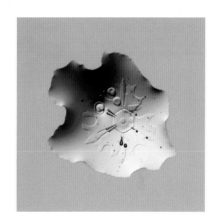

Evaporation and Melting

The top series of pictures shows a snow crystal slowly evaporating away under the lights of the microscope. From left to right, a period of two minutes elapsed. You can see how the finer features and extremities are the first to disappear, leaving behind a simpler shape. Snowflakes are always at their best when they are freshly fallen.

The lower series was taken when the temperature was just below freezing, so the crystal evaporated at first and then simply melted. For these pictures, just 27 seconds elapsed from left to right. It can be quite a challenge to photograph in such warm conditions.

Snow crystals are always changing, and they usually begin evaporating as soon as they stop growing. If the clouds are high, the crystals may evaporate significantly before they even hit the ground, which is what happened to the specimen at left. Note the rounded contours without sharp facets, almost as if the edges had been worn smooth with age.

Once on the ground, snowflakes lose their finer features quickly. After a few days in a snowbank, the crystals are mostly blocky in form, showing little of their initial elaborate structures.

January 18, 2005: Houghton, Michigan

I encountered a remarkable variety of snow crystal types today. The temperature was warming throughout the day, from about -18 degrees Celsius (0 degrees Fahrenheit) in the early morning to -8 degrees Celsius (18 degrees Fahrenheit) in the late afternoon, accompanied by a gentle wind from the southeast. The snowfall was light throughout the day. Most of the snow was small and grainy, but many well-formed crystals were in the mix. Small plates, stellar plates and dendrites, hollow columns, and slender needles were all waiting to be discovered, along with a good number of sizable capped columns.

Lake Superior dominates the winter climate in the Upper Peninsula, as the mist rising from the unfrozen lake feeds the clouds at a prodigious rate. This is classic lake-effect snow, producing about an inch of snowfall per day. Although there are gems to be found on good days, most of the crystals are small and granular. At night, the street lights frequently reveal almost no sparkle in the newly fallen snow, indicating crystals with few large, well-formed facets.

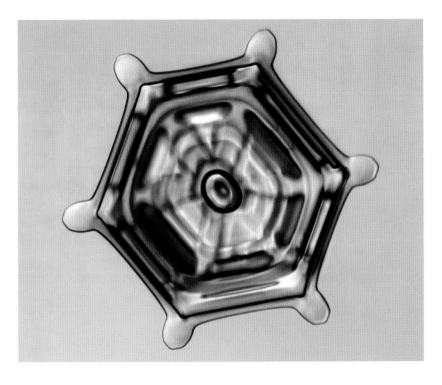

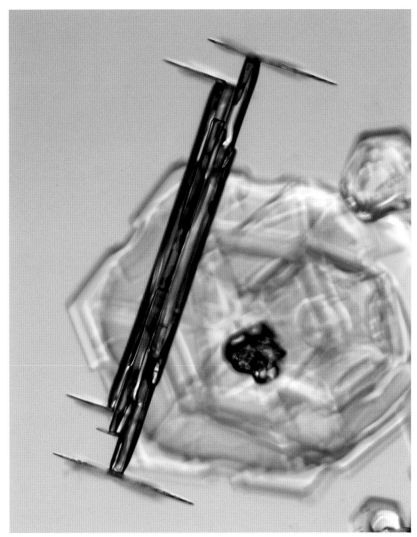

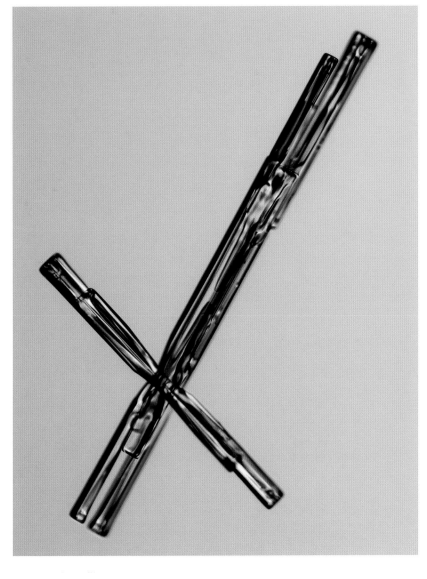

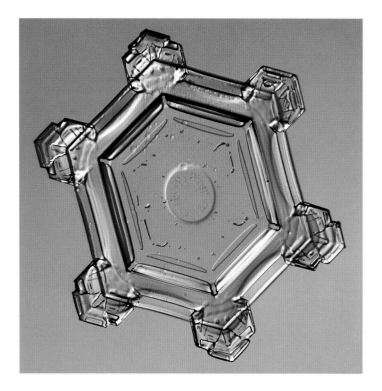
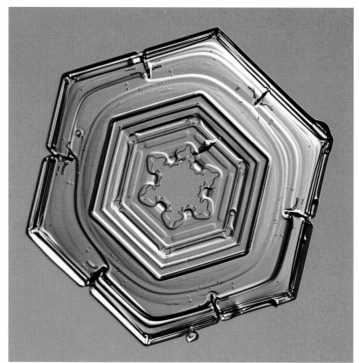

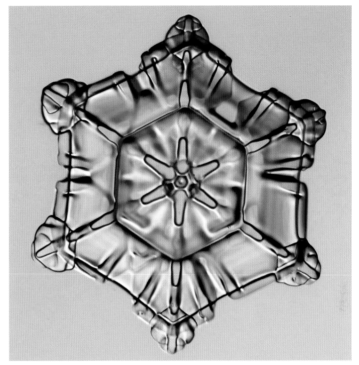

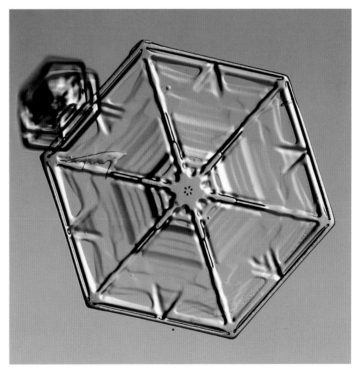

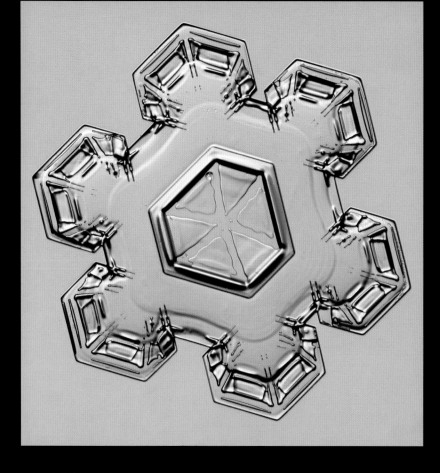
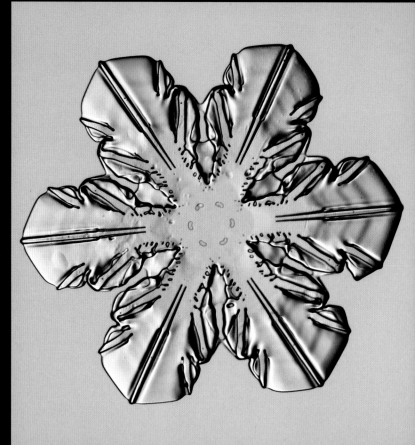

My attention was caught by a snowflake on my coat-sleeve. It was one of those perfect little pine trees in shape, arranged around a central spangle. This little object, which, with many of its fellows, rested unmelting on my coat, so perfect and beautiful, reminded me that Nature had not lost her pristine vigor yet, and why should man lose heart?

—Henry David Thoreau (1817–1862)

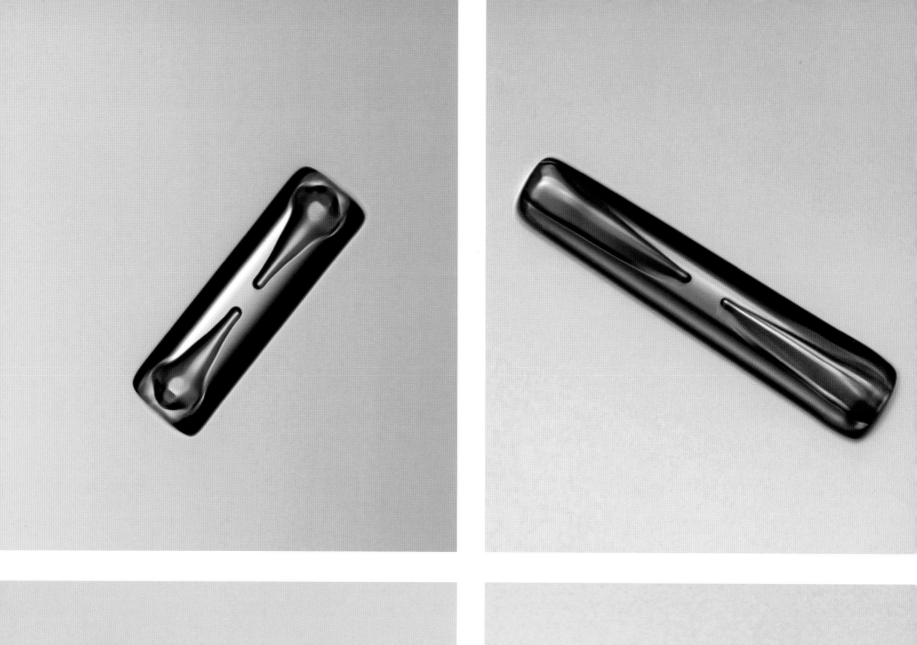

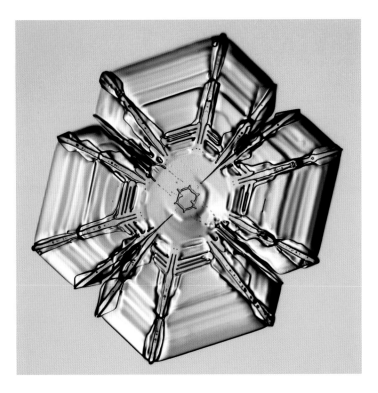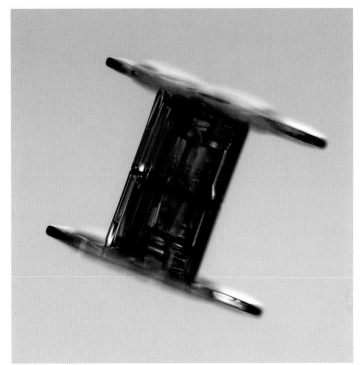

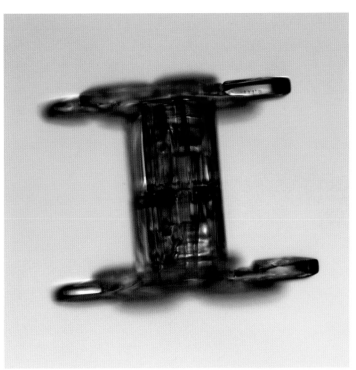

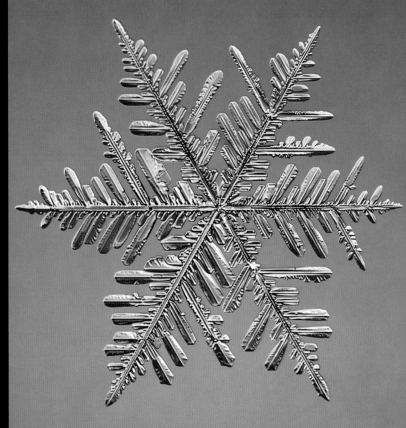

When the temperature of the air is within a degree or two of the freezing point, and much snow falls, it frequently consists of large irregular flakes . . . . But in severe frosts . . . the most regular and beautiful forms are always seen floating in the air, and sparkling in the sun-beams; and the snow which falls in general is of the most elegant texture and appearance.

—William Scoresby (1760–1829)

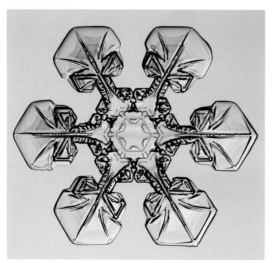

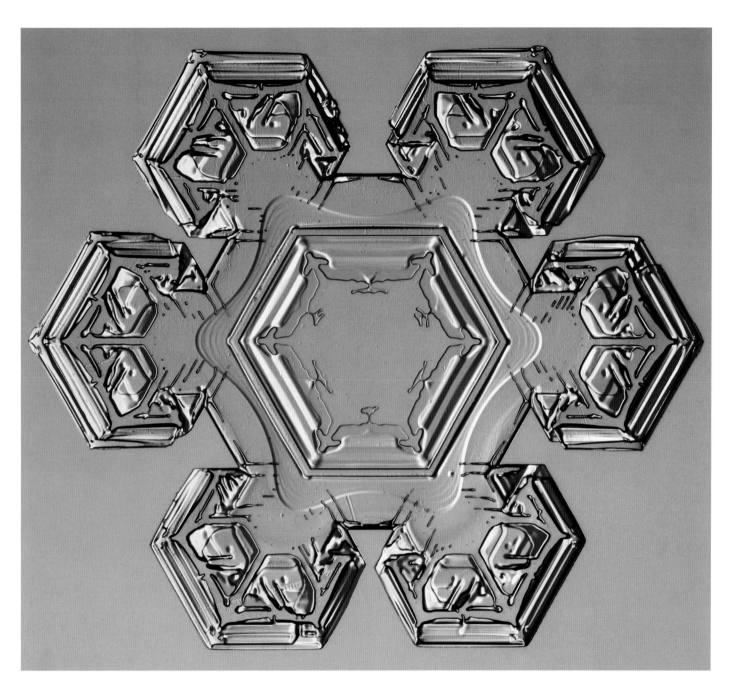

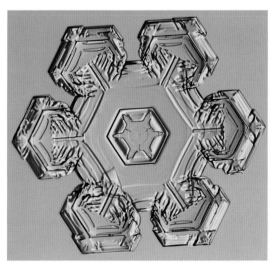

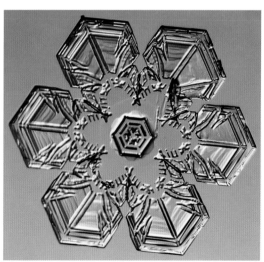

February 7, 2005: Cochrane, Ontario

For most of the past week, the temperature was above freezing and getting warmer—yesterday's high was 7 degrees Celsius (45 degrees Fahrenheit). The locals were delighted at the balmy conditions, but I felt just the opposite. Instead of gorgeous snow crystals we got bland drizzle and rain. It was beginning to look as if my trip would end before I could take a single photograph.

Yesterday, however, it became apparent that winter was not over yet. The forecast called for a sharp temperature drop as a front passed overhead. During the night, the temperature shot down to -10 degrees Celsius (14 degrees Fahrenheit) in just a few hours. The timing worked well for me, as a nice snowfall began just as it got light this morning. I found many wonderfully sculpted crystals of all different types, from stellar plates and dendrites to needles and capped columns. There were even a few sheaths, cups, triangular crystals, and other exotic forms mixed in. I worked this wonderful snowfall all day and took nearly 250 photographs.

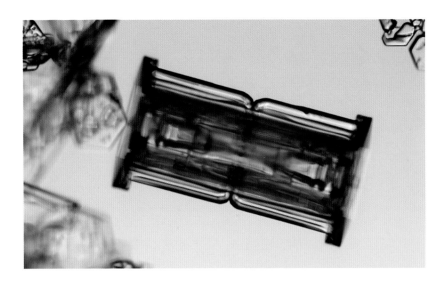

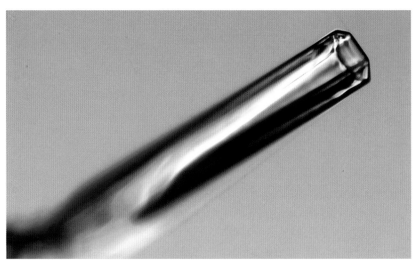

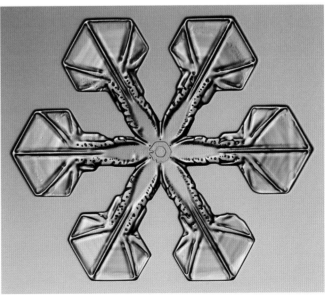

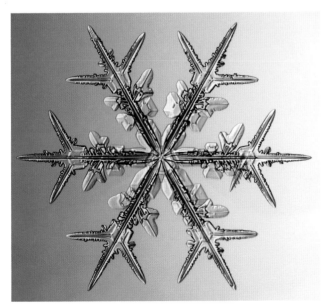

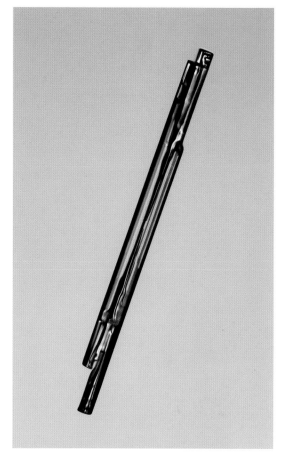

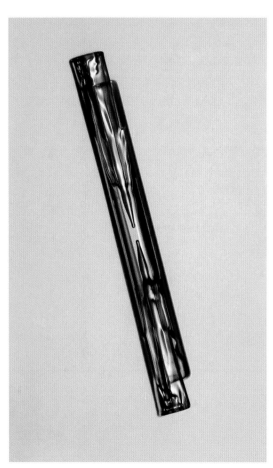

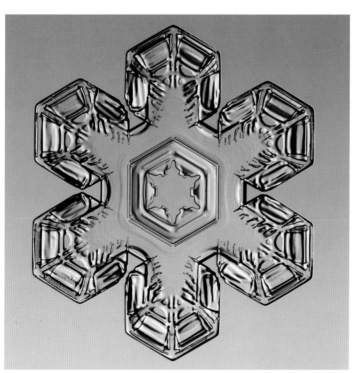

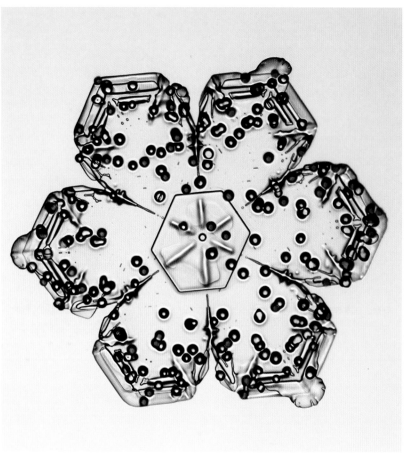

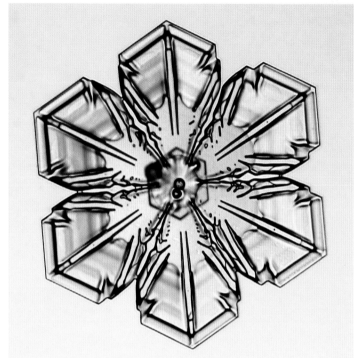

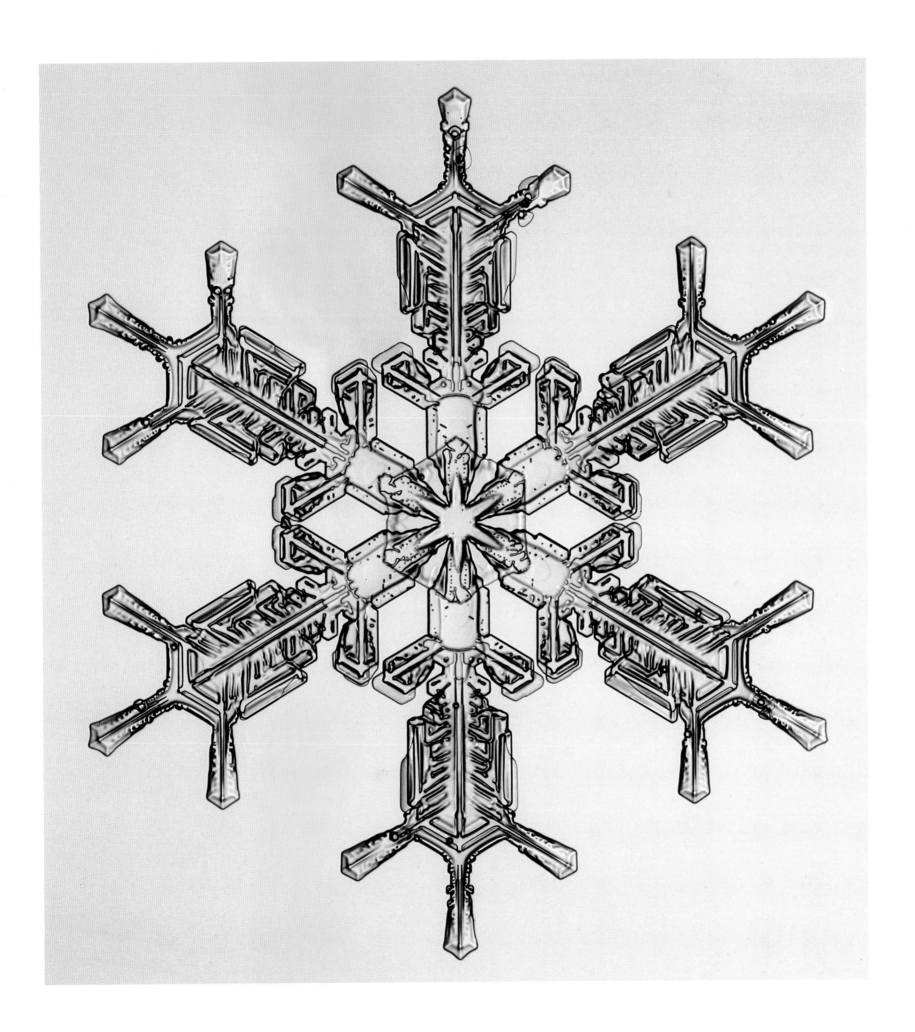

The beauty of a snow-crystal depends on its mathematical regularity and symmetry; but somehow the association of many variants of a single type, all related but no two the same, vastly increases our pleasure and admiration . . . . The snow-crystal is further complicated, and its beauty is notably enhanced, by minute occluded bubbles of air or drops of water, whose symmetrical form and arrangement are very curious and not always easy to explain. Lastly, we are apt to see our snow crystals after a slight thaw has rounded their edges, and has heightened their beauty by softening their contours.

—D'Arcy Wentworth Thompson (1860–1948)

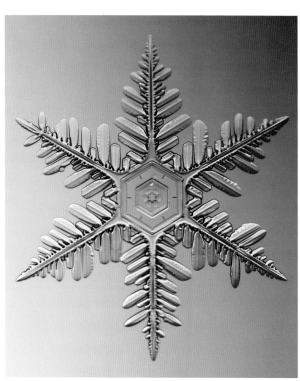

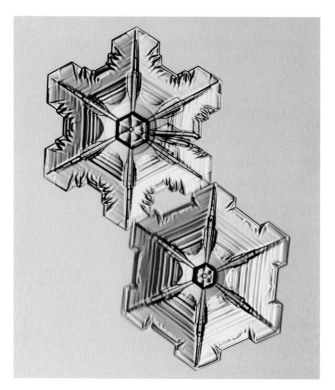

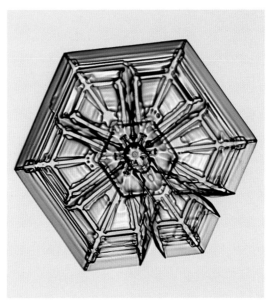

109

Commonly the flakes reach us travel-worn and agglomerated, comparatively without order or beauty, far down in their fall, like men in their advanced age.

—Henry David Thoreau (1817–1862)

December 27, 2005: Cochrane, Ontario

I pulled into town this afternoon in the midst of a warm, wet, blowing snowfall. Conditions were far from ideal, and many crystals were coated with rime. Nevertheless, I set up to take what pictures I could. It was a difficult session, as blowing snow got into everything and the crystals melted rapidly under the bright lights of my microscope. There was a plus side to these conditions, however, as I found that the colored lights played nicely off the deformed surfaces, giving the crystals a distinctly fluid look. Even these travel-worn snowflakes are interesting to view at high magnification, and each has its own unique story to tell of its fall through the clouds.

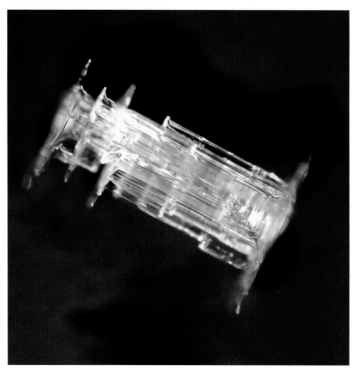

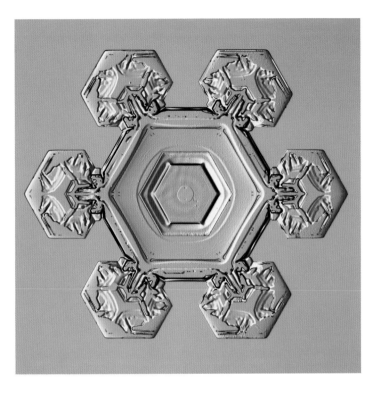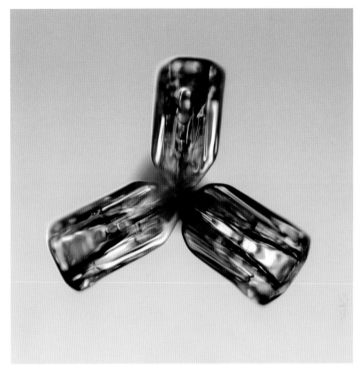

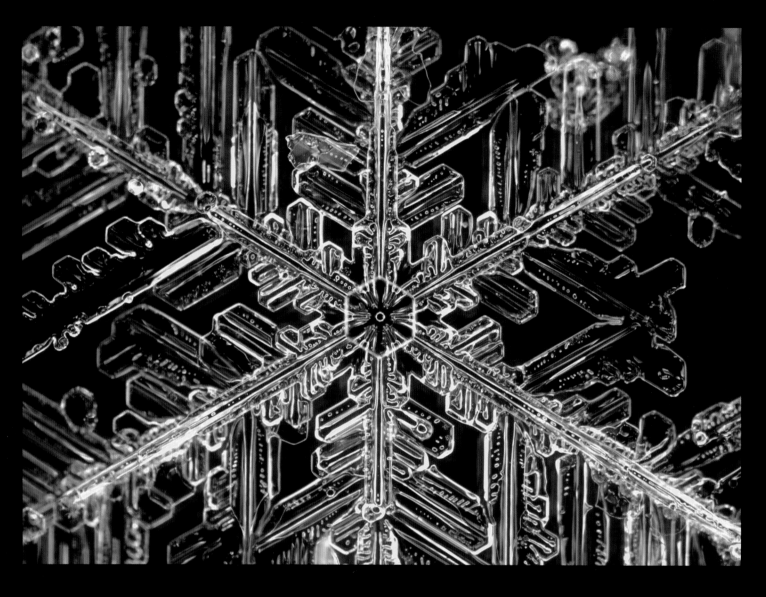

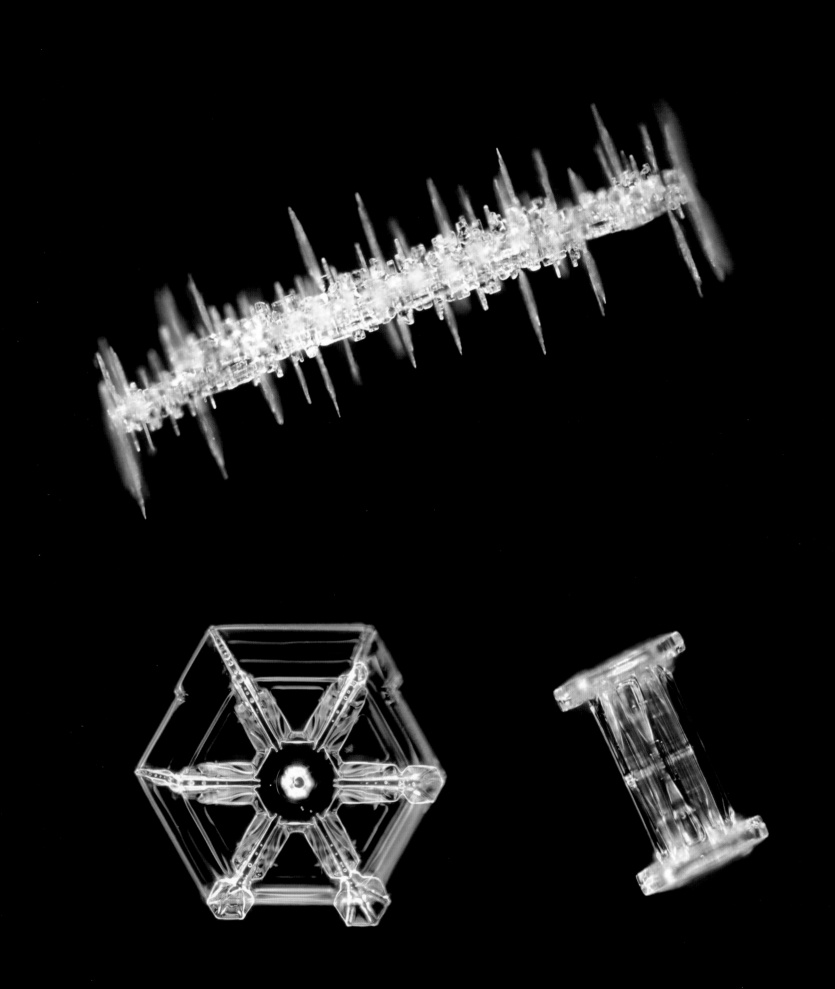

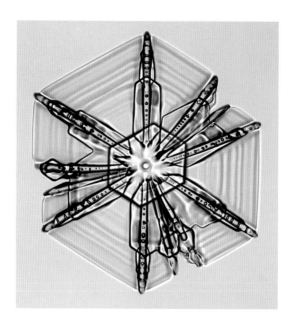

January 2, 2006: Cochrane, Ontario

I got out early this cold morning to photograph the sun rising through the treetops. It was a colorful display, as the sky glowed a rich crimson just before daybreak.

While taking in the scene, I noticed a distinct light pillar caused by countless tiny ice crystals sparkling in the low morning sun. I found myself in the midst of a gentle snowfall, even though there wasn't a cloud in the sky. The crystals were barely notice-able on my sleeve, as most were less than half a millimeter (0.02 inches) in size. They were nicely faceted, however, so I quickly set up my microscope to take some pictures of this striking diamond dust.

Some of the crystals were almost perfectly hexagonal with razor-sharp facets, and all had pronounced skeletal ribs. Many looked a bit like insects with angular shells made from partial ice plates. The crystals became smaller as the sun climbed higher, disappearing altogether after about an hour.

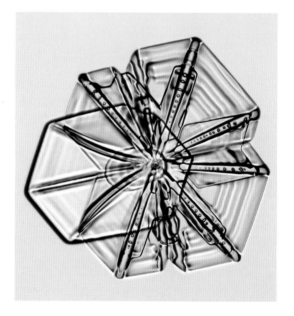

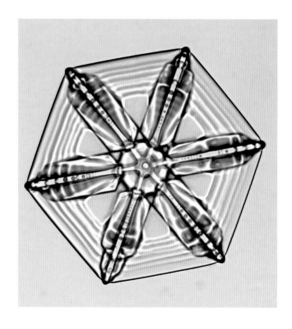

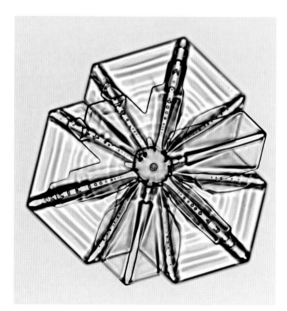

If there is no wind to disturb their descent, plate-like snow crystals tend to fall with their faces nearly horizontal to the ground. Reflections from these aligned crystals can produce a "pillar" of light extending above and below the sun. The vertical light pillar at left is not a camera artifact, but is caused by the combined sparkle of many faceted ice crystals. Against the dark trees below the sun, you can make out some bright specks that are reflections from individual crystals.

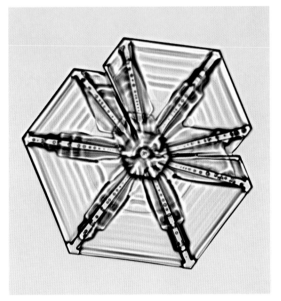

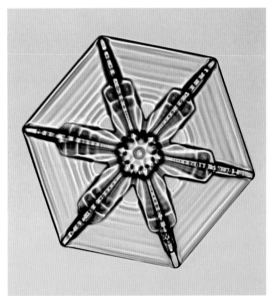

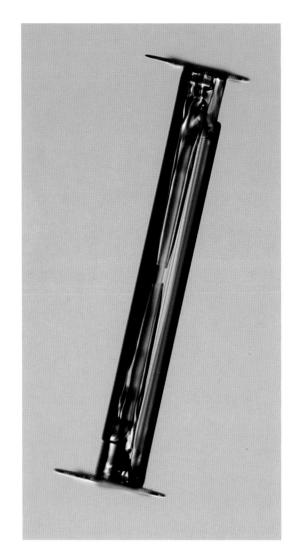

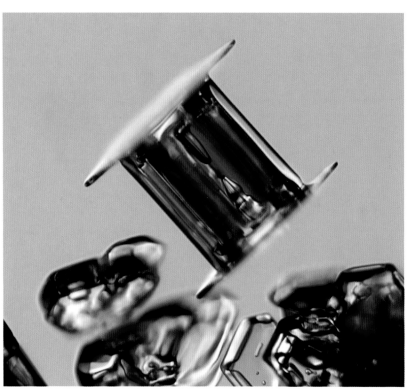

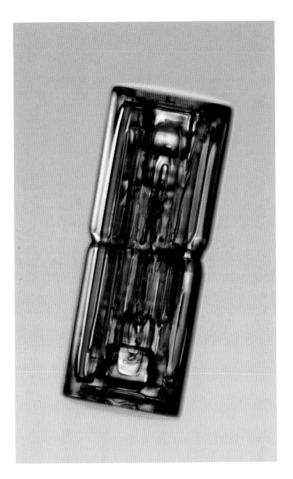

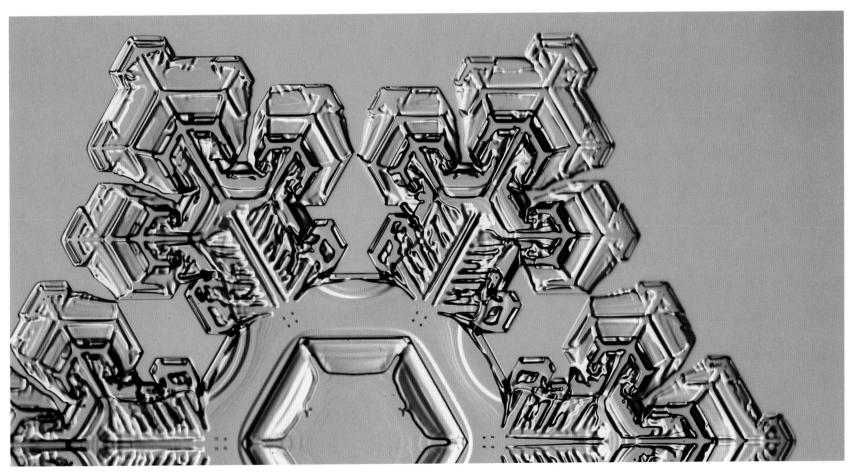

January 3, 2006: Cochrane, Ontario

The scene was cold and overcast this morning, the kind of monotone winter day where the sky and ground are both a uniform grey. Some light flurries arrived soon after breakfast, bringing mostly small stellar crystals, each with six simple spokes emanating from its center. It was remarkable how similar they all appeared by eye. At one point I had about a hundred thousand of these tiny stars overlapping one another on my collection board.

In just the ten minutes it took to set up my camera, the snowfall changed its character and started dropping mostly broad-branched plates. They were still small, little more than a millimeter in size, but many were quite symmetrical with well-formed facets. A good number were double plates, as could be seen when I happened to get an edge-on view. The crystals looked like simple mirrors sparkling on my sleeve, but the microscope revealed their intricate surface patterns.

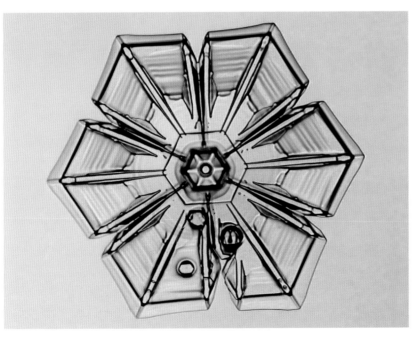

January 5, 2006: Cochrane, Ontario

Today could only be described as the perfect snowfall. The temperature hovered around -13 degrees Celsius (8 degrees Fahrenheit), which is ideal for finding broad-branched stellar crystals. It snowed lightly all day with no wind, and the clouds hung low in the sky, just above ground level, so the crystals formed directly overhead. It felt as if I was inside the crystal nursery, watching as snowflakes were growing all around.

The clouds were patchy as they drifted by, which resulted in considerable variation in the crystal patterns that formed. This wonderful confluence of meteorological conditions produced a wealth of spectacular, diverse, large stellar crystals that fell throughout the day. It was as if Nature was focusing her considerable skills on creating her most outstanding snow crystals. I worked the falling snow all day and took more than 800 photographs.

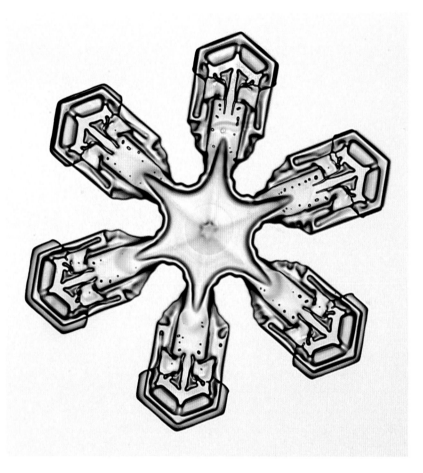

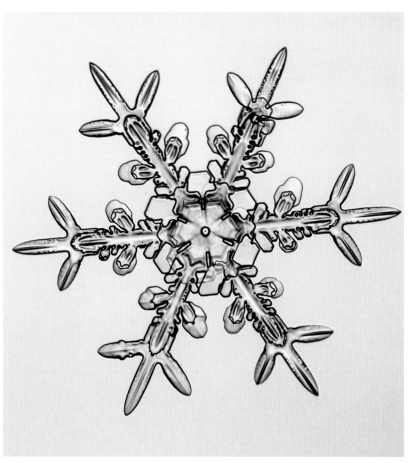

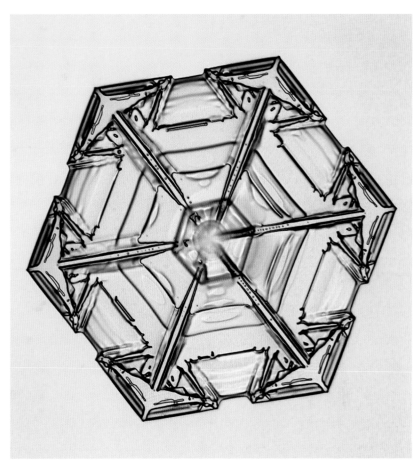

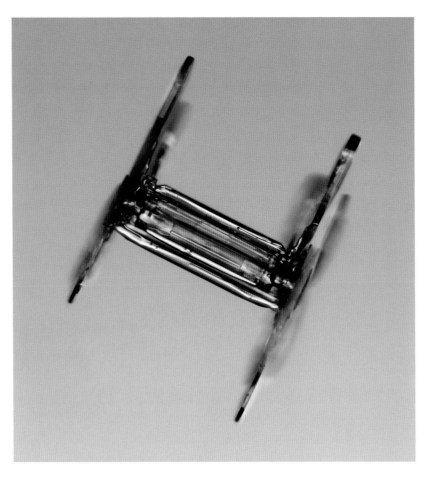

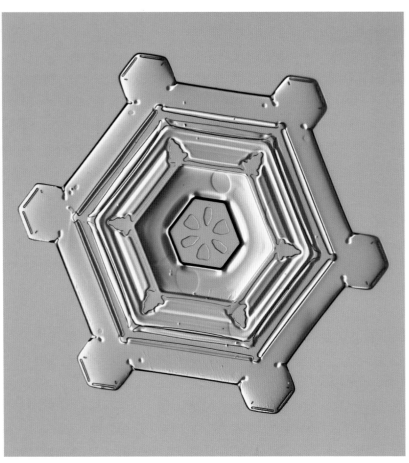

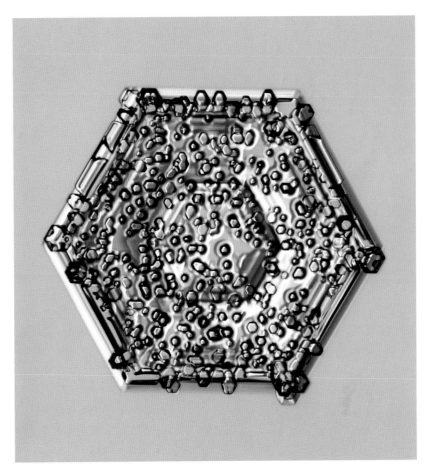

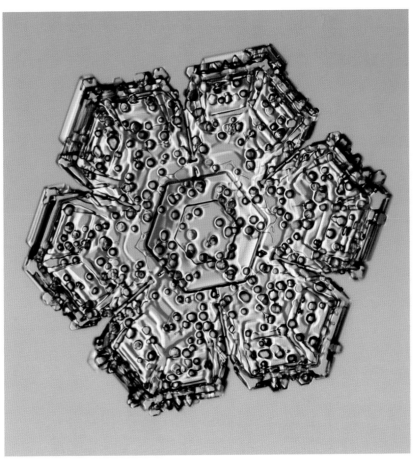

January 25, 2006: Cochrane, Ontario

The forecast was not calling for any precipitation overnight, but my internal snow alarm must have awakened me around 3 a.m. When I looked out the window, I saw what appeared to be a respectable snowfall, so I pulled on my many layers of clothes to have a better look. It was bitter cold outside, but the crystals looked nice, so I set up my camera in the darkness.

Before long the snowfall brought some exceptionally large and thick stellar dendrites. Many were over 5 mm (0.2 inches) in diameter and nicely formed. I found some huge double plates mixed in as well. The thickness of the crystals gave them a pleasing look under the microscope.

I had a productive photo session, even though there was only a small porch light to work under. By about 6 a.m., still long before sunrise at this latitude, the snowfall stopped and I noticed an abundance of twinkling stars in the now cloudless sky overhead.

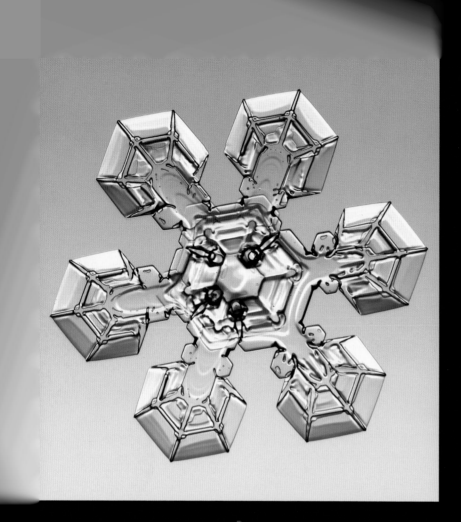 

 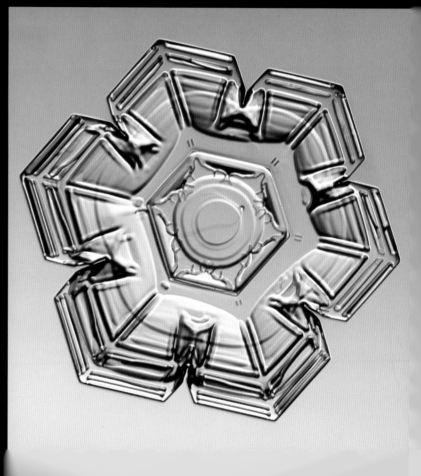

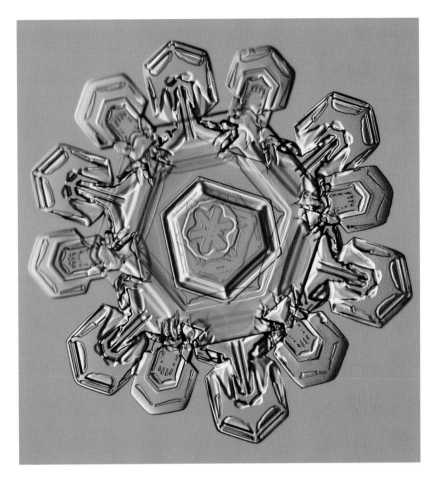

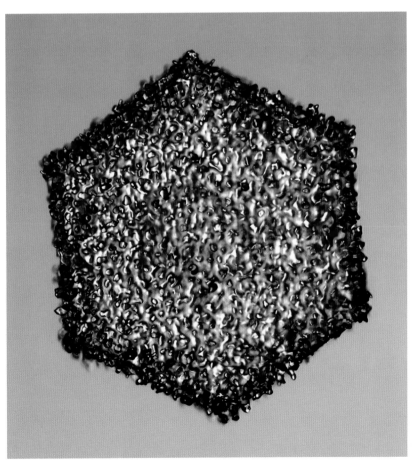

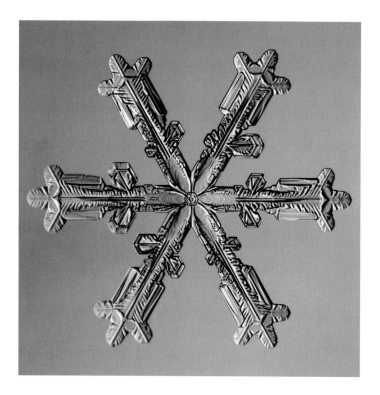

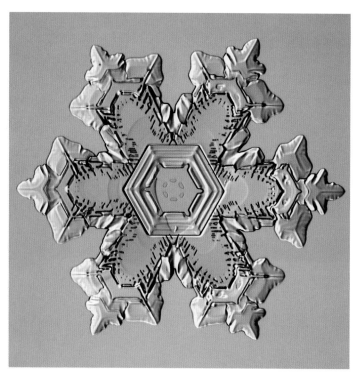
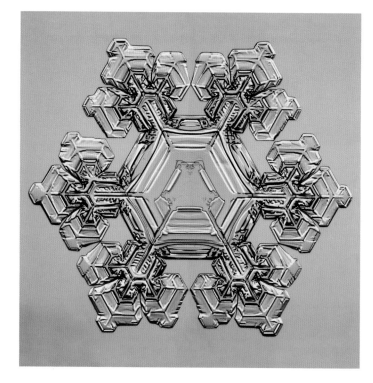

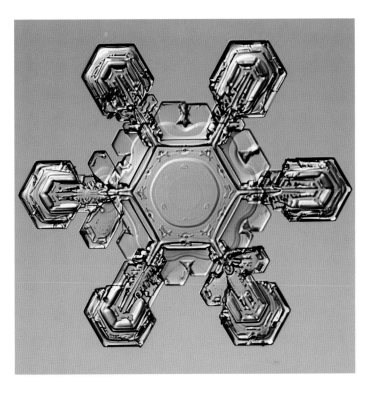

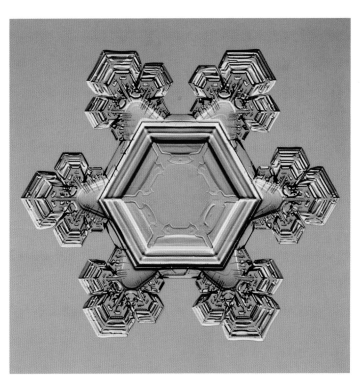

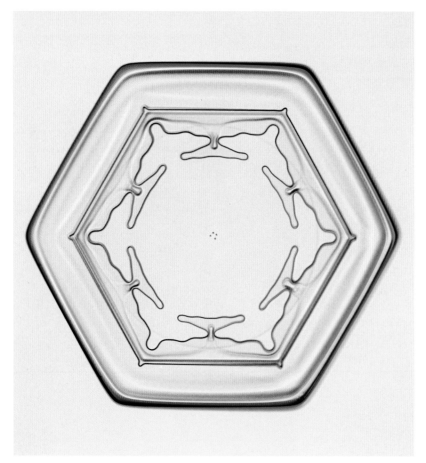

138

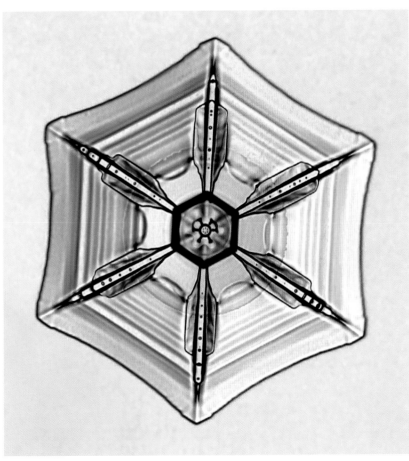

There is nothing in the world more beautiful than the forest clothed to its very hollows in snow. It is the still ecstasy of nature, wherein every spray, every blade of grass, every spire of reed, every intricacy of twig, is clad with radiance.

—Fiona Macleod (1855–1905)

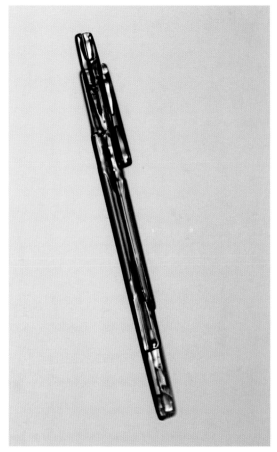

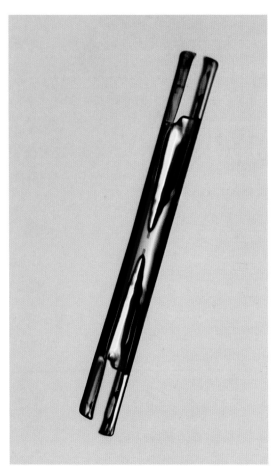

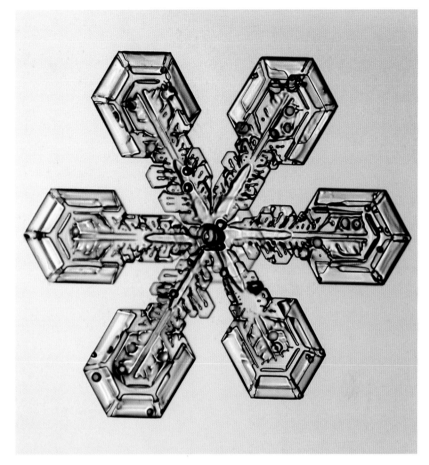

The thin snow now driving from the north and lodging on my coat consists of those beautiful star crystals, not cottony and chubby spokes . . . but thin and partly transparent crystals. They are about a tenth of an inch in diameter, perfect little wheels with six spokes without a tire, or rather with six perfect little leaflets, fernlike, with a distinct straight and slender midrib, raying out from the center. On each side of each midrib there is a transparent thin blade with a crenate edge. How full of the creative genius is the air in which these are generated! I should hardly admire more if real stars fell and lodged on my coat. Nature is full of genius, full of the divinity; so that not a snowflake escapes its fashioning hand. Nothing is cheap and coarse, neither dewdrops nor snowflakes.

—Henry David Thoreau (1817–1862)

154

About the Author

Kenneth Libbrecht was raised in North Dakota and educated at Caltech and Princeton, receiving his PhD in physics in 1984. He subsequently joined the faculty at Caltech, where he is currently professor of physics and chairman of the physics department. Dr. Libbrecht has published numerous scientific articles on a range of topics, including the free oscillations of the sun and stars, ultra-cold atomic gases, the detection of gravitational radiation, and the mechanics of crystal growth. He is also the author of *The Snowflake: Winter's Secret Beauty*, *The Little Book of Snowflakes*, and *Ken Libbrecht's Field Guide to Snowflakes*, all published by Voyageur Press. He resides in Pasadena, California, with his wife and two children. More information about snow crystals can be found at his website, *www.snowcrystals.com*.

About the Photographs

The photographs in this book are of natural snowflakes, created in the winter clouds and captured by the author as they fell to earth. Colored lighting was used to create a variety of visual effects, exploiting the refractive properties of the clear ice crystals. The images were digitally edited slightly to remove minor blemishes which otherwise distract from the natural patterns and structures. In particular, spots in the background areas, caused by bits of dust on the camera sensor or glass slides, were removed from most pictures. Some images of larger crystals were digitally stitched together from multiple photographs. Brightness, contrast, color balance, and other global parameters were adjusted somewhat for artistic effect.

 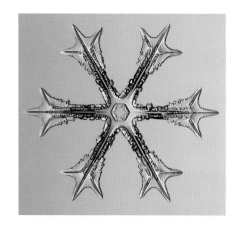 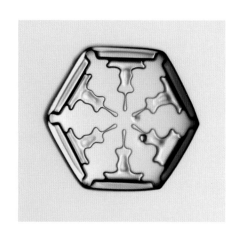

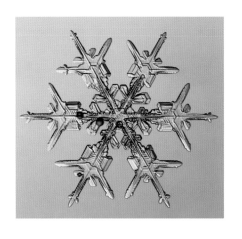 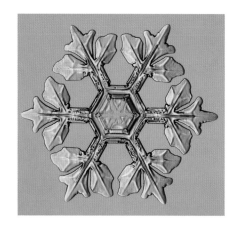 

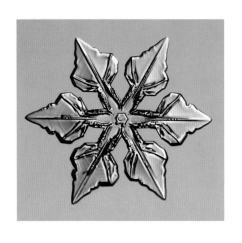 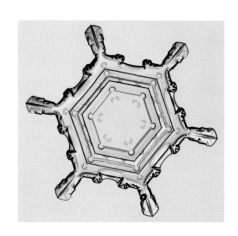 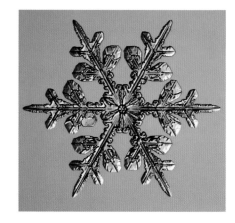